Name

Score

5

4

Candyfloss

Every year, thousands of people visit Blackpool.

Blackpool has a massive tower that looks out over the

1 ☐ .... The tower has been there for over a

1 ☐ hundred years. The rest of the .... has

changed a lot since then.

1 ☐ Nowadays .... are so many things to do in

1 ☐ Blackpool, it would take .... to see everything.

1 ☐ You can go on the biggest roller .... in the

1 ☐ country. You can .... around a track in a

go-kart, or go right up to the top of Blackpool Tower itself.

Part 2

If it is .... or cold, you can go .... -

skating. You can also go rock-climbing and trampolining

....

Most of the outdoor .... are closed in

.... , but you can pretend that it is still summer

at Sandcastle Water World. There are deep blue

..........................., waterfalls and huge ....

At Blackpool, you can .... candyfloss even in the

middle of winter. Just make .... you keep it out

of the rain.

Spelling Mark	
out of 20 for parts 1 and 2	

Set B — Spelling
Candyfloss

**Practice
question**

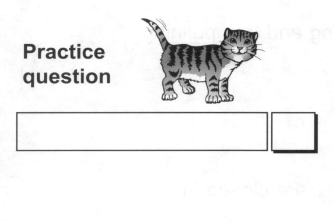

1

2

3

Set A — Level 3 Reading
Question Booklet
The Grateful Crane & Japan

FIRST NAME	

SCORE		LEVEL	

Practice questions

page 2

A. What did the man hear when he was out hunting?

....

....

B. Where did the man find the crane?

☐ in a tree ☐ in a field

☐ in the road ☐ in some grass

These questions are about *The Grateful Crane*.

1. How did the man free the crane?

   ....

   ....

1 mark

2. What did the man do as the crane flew away?

   ☐ walked home   ☐ packed his bag

   ☐ watched it fly away   ☐ set the trap

1 mark

3. Why was it strange that there was a knock on the door that night?

   ....

   ....

1 mark

4. Why were the villagers happy?

   ....

   ....

1 mark

5.   Why did the man get a high price for the cloth?

....

....

1 mark

6.   "...the colours shone more brightly than the feathers of a peacock..."
       Why do you think the author describes the cloth in this way?

....

....

1 mark

Questions on page 5 of the story

7.   What did the neighbours think was strange?

....

....

1 mark

Questions on page 6 of the story

8.   Do you think that the man was wrong to look into the weaving room?

       ☐   yes   ☐   no

       Why? ....

....

2 marks

THE GRATEFUL CRANE

9.   How does the man's life change after he meets Tsu?

....

....

1 mark

10.   Why did the crane return to the young man?

....

....

1 mark

11. (a)   The story starts with the crane flying away and the man watching it.
How do you think the man would feel at the end of the story when he watches the crane fly away again?

....

....

1 mark

(b)   Why would he have this feeling?

....

....

1 mark

These questions are about *Japan*.

12.　What does the red circle on the Japanese flag mean?

....

....

1 mark

13.　What do the Japanese call their country?

....

....

1 mark

Questions on pages 4 and 5 of the information booklet.

14.　Write down one way that a man's kimono is different from a woman's.

....

....

1 mark

15.　What is an *obi*?

☐　a Japanese dress　　　　☐　Japanese shoes

☐　a long belt　　　　　　　☐　a bow

1 mark

16. Why should you remember your table manners in Japan?

....

....

1 mark

17. How could you practise using chopsticks?

....

....

1 mark

18. What should you do in Japan if you are eating noodles?

....

1 mark

Why? ....

....

1 mark

19.   What sort of fish does the sushi recipe suggest you use?

....

1 mark

20.   What do you use to roll up sushi?

....

....

1 mark

Questions on the whole of the information booklet.

21.   A Japanese woman might wear a kimono.
    Write down two other things she may wear with her kimono.

    1.   ....

    2.   ....

1 mark

22.   If you wanted to find out about meals in Japan,
    which page would be most useful?

    ....

1 mark

[BLANK PAGE]

Set B — Level 3 Reading
Information Booklet
Teamwork in Nature

Contents

Introduction 2

Bee Facts 4

Ant Facts 6

Introduction

Ants and bees are insects that often live in groups.
In a group of bees, different bees will have different
jobs. That way, each bee is helping the whole group,
instead of just looking after itself.

Bee Facts

 There are over 20 000 different types of bee.

 Honeybees live and work together in large groups called colonies.

 The nest that the colony of bees lives in is called a hive. It is made from wax that the bees produce themselves.

Worker bees build the hive for the colony and collect food for all the bees. They make honey and store it in holes in the hive.

 The Queen bee has the job of laying eggs that grow into new bees. She can lay 1500 eggs in a single day.

 There is only one Queen bee in each hive.

 If the Queen bee gets too hot or too cold, she will not be able to lay enough eggs. If the Queen is cold, more worker bees go near her to keep her warm. If she is hot, they will move further away.

Ant Facts

 Like bees, ants also work together by doing different jobs.

 The soldier ants defend the ant colony from attack. Soldier ants are large and fierce.

 The ants who go looking for food are called worker ants. They are smaller than the soldier ants.

 Some worker ants have the job of looking after the eggs until the baby ants hatch.

Ants eat plants, nectar and other insects. They work as a team to carry heavy pieces of food.

 Honey ants keep insects called aphids in their nests. The worker ants look after the aphids and collect a sweet liquid called honeydew from them.

 Army ants are a type of ant that cling together at night to make a living nest out of their bodies.

EHP11

Set A — Level 3 Reading
Information Booklet
Japan

The Japanese Flag

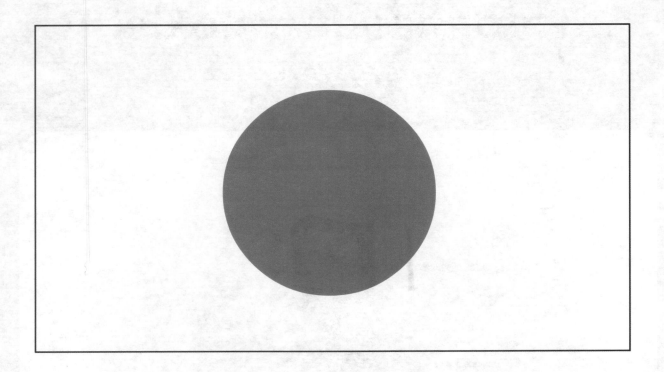

The Japanese flag is a large red circle on a white
background. The red circle represents the Sun.
The white background means 'purity'.

JAPAN

Sapporo

Sendai

Tokyo

Kitakyushu   Osaka

Japan is sometimes known as 'The Land of the Rising Sun'.
This is what the Japanese call their country.

Clothes in Japan

Japanese traditional dress is the *kimono*. There are many different styles such as smart kimonos, summer kimonos and kimonos for children. There are even kimonos for lazing around at home!

kimono

obi

Women's kimonos often have beautiful patterns in bright colours.

It is difficult to put on a kimono yourself. After wrapping the kimono around your body, it is held together with a long belt called an *obi*. You need a friend to tie a bow at the back for you.

Men's kimonos are very different. They are shorter and the patterns are not as colourful. You wear the kimono over trousers. It folds across your body and then you tie it up with an *obi*. Men fasten it up by themselves by tying the knot on one side.

These strange shoes are called *geta*. They make you tall to protect your kimono from the dirt in the street.

Eating in Japan

In Japan, people eat rice with almost every meal.
Their food is healthy, with lots of vegetables and fish.
Japanese people usually use chopsticks to eat. They can
be quite difficult to use at first. Japanese people are very
polite – so make sure you remember your table manners!

In Japan, it is not bad manners
to slurp when you eat noodles.
In fact, they would think it
strange if you were quiet!

Try eating Smarties
with chopsticks!

Get an adult to show you how to use chopsticks
and then practise picking up and eating Smarties.
Try it as a challenge!

Recipe
Sushi

You will need:

4 cupfuls of cooked rice
1 tin of salmon or tuna fish
4 sheets of dried seaweed
2 tbsp sweetcorn
1tbsp mayonnaise

clean, dry tea-towel
table spoons
sharp knife

Method:

1. Mix the fish, sweetcorn and mayonnaise.
2. Put a seaweed sheet on the tea-towel.
   Spread rice over half the sheet.
   Put a row of tuna mixture on the rice.

3. Use the tea-towel to roll the sushi over once.
   Squeeze the roll gently.

4. Roll the sushi up completely.

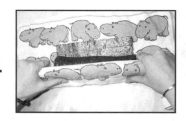

5. Check the roll is tightly closed.
   Ask an adult to help you slice it into smaller rolls.
   Place the sushi rolls flat on a plate.
   Repeat for each sheet of seaweed.

[BLANK PAGE]

Set B — Level 2 Reading
The Sea

Name

Score

Level and grade

Exam Set EHP11

Pirates' Treasure

One sunny day in the summer holidays, Marla-May danced out of her large white house by the sea. She put on her pirate hat and eye-patch, and set off with Scruffy to find treasure.

Scruffy was the family dog. He was small and bouncy, with a short stubby tail. Marla-May liked nothing better than exploring the beach with Scruffy.

PRACTICE QUESTIONS

A   What did Marla-May put on when she left the house?

....

B   Marla-May liked nothing better than

☐ going swimming in the sea ☐ playing outside on nice days

☐ eating pancakes for breakfast ☐ going exploring with the dog

Round and round they ran on the beach, sorting through the flotsam and jetsam and saving pretty pieces of coloured glass.

Breathless with laughter, Marla-May sat down hard. Scruffy dug frantically at the edge of the sea.

It wasn't long before he came towards her with a sandy little bottle in his mouth.

1   What did Marla save from the beach?

    .... ☐

2   What did Scruffy find in the sand?

    .... ☐

"What have you got there, boy?" asked Marla-May.

She opened the bottle and pulled out a sheet of paper. She gasped in amazement. There was a map drawn on the paper and Marla-May realised it showed the very beach they were on. She could even see her house and their old boathouse on the map.

On the map, right at the back of the boathouse, there was a red cross.

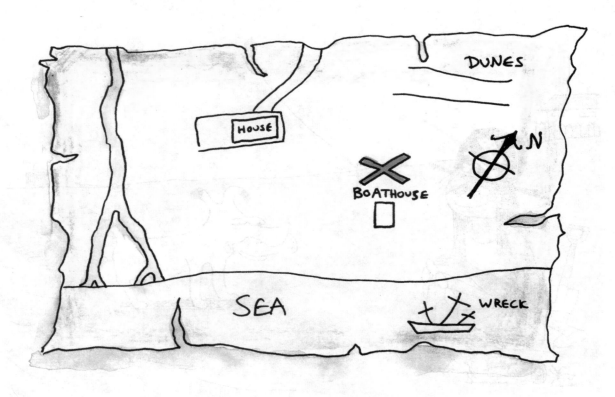

3   What did Marla-May find in the bottle?

....

4   Why was Marla-May amazed?

☐ she thought she had
found a treasure map

☐ because she was going
to see the old boathouse

☐ she really enjoyed
digging

☐ because it was the
summer holidays

"Treasure!" squeaked Marla-May. "It's a treasure map. Come on Scruffy, let's go and dig it up straight away."

They dug, and dug, and dug. Marla-May used a spade and Scruffy used his paws. Soon they were both covered in mud and tired, but they still hadn't found any treasure, just a pile of stones.

5   How do you think Marla-May felt when she squeaked "Treasure!".

☐ excited   ☐ scared

☐ angry   ☐ miserable

6   Write down **2** things Scruffy and Marla-May used to dig.

a)   ....

b)   ....

Marla-May's mother called her in for tea. While she ate, Marla-May explained about the map and the treasure she couldn't find and how disappointed she was.

"Never mind," said her mother. "Bath and bed now, and have another look first thing tomorrow morning. I'm sure you'll find some treasure."

Next morning, Marla-May ran down to the boathouse before breakfast and started digging again.

7   Why did Marla-May's mother call her in?

.... ☐

8   Why do you think Marla-May was disappointed?

☐ she had to
come in to bed

☐ Scruffy had to
have a bath

☐ she wasn't allowed
crumpets for tea

☐ she hadn't found
any treasure   ☐

9   What other thing does Marla-May's mother say to cheer her up?

a) ....*Never mind*..........................

b) .... ☐

10   Why do you think Marla-May didn't have any
breakfast before she began digging in the morning?

☐ she was too excited
about finding treasure

☐ you are more likely to find
treasure first thing in the morning

☐ she wasn't hungry

☐ she liked to run around
before breakfast   ☐

Almost straight away she found a strange square package. She rushed back to the house with it screaming and shrieking, "I've found treasure."

"L...l...l..look, TREASURE!"

In the kitchen she sat down with her mother and unwrapped the parcel. Her hands were shaking. Inside some plastic was a wooden box. She opened the lid and up popped a parrot, which span round and round as music played.

"Wow! This must be real pirates' treasure," said Marla-May. But her mother just smiled quietly.

11 Why did Marla-May scream and shriek?

.... □

12 Why do you think **'look'** is written as 'l...l..l.look'?

□ because Marla-May screamed it very loudly

□ to show that Marla-May was very nervous and excited

□ so you can see it is very important

□ because there was lots of treasure

□

13 What do you think it was about the music box that made Marla-May think it must be **real pirates' treasure**?

....

....

□
□

14 Why do you think Marla-May's mother **just smiled quietly**?

□ she didn't like parrots

□ she hid the treasure there for Marla-May overnight

□ she couldn't think of anything good to say

□ she thought Marla-May was being too loud

□

Oceans and Ships

This part of the booklet is about oceans and pirate ships.

You will read about

- the oceans of the world

- how people were once afraid of sea monsters

- how a pirate ship sails on the sea.

PRACTICE QUESTIONS

A   What is the next part of the booklet about?

Sand ☐   Oceans ☐

Parrots ☐   Treasure ☐

B   What were people once afraid of?

....

The World's Oceans

Nearly three quarters of the Earth's surface is covered by water.

The oceans are made of salt water.

---

15   How much of the Earth's surface is covered by water?

nearly a half ☐

nearly three
quarters ☐

nearly all ☐

nearly one quarter ☐   ☐

16   What are the oceans made of?

....   ☐

There are three main oceans. They are called the Pacific Ocean, the Atlantic Ocean and the Indian Ocean.

The three main oceans are all joined together, so there's really only one big ocean.

The deepest part of the ocean is the Mariana Trench. It is a very deep underwater valley near the coast of Japan. It is 11 034 metres deep.

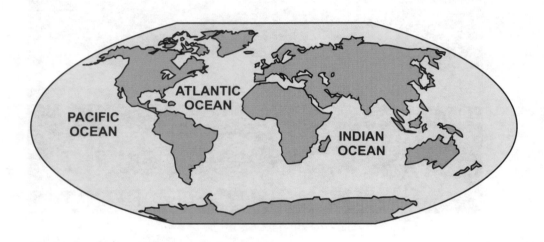

17 What are the names of the three main oceans?

   Pacific Ocean,
   ....

18 What is the deepest part of the ocean called?

   ....

19 How deep is it?

   ....

Sea Monsters

Hundreds of years ago, people thought that sea monsters lived in the ocean. Nobody sailed very far from land because they were afraid of the sea monsters.

People believed that there was a kind of giant octopus called a Kraken. They thought it could drag a boat underwater.

20 Where did people think that the sea monsters lived?

   ....

21 Why didn't people want to sail far from the land?

   ....

22 What kind of monster was the Kraken?

   ....

Pirate Ships

A pirate ship has sails to catch the wind.
The wind blows the ship across the water.
If the pirates want to go faster they put up more sails.

A Pirate Ship

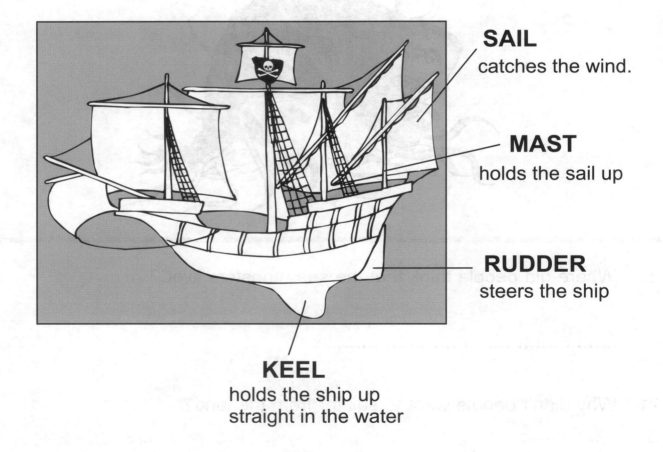

SAIL
catches the wind.

MAST
holds the sail up

RUDDER
steers the ship

KEEL
holds the ship up
straight in the water

23   What is the sail on the pirate ship for?

to catch the waves ☐   to make a noise ☐

to catch the wind ☐   to make the
                                        wind blow ☐   ☐

24   What will happen if the pirates put up more sails?

....   ☐

25   What does the rudder do?

....   ☐

26   What holds the sails up?

....   ☐

[BLANK PAGE]

They didn't even notice this bit.

Set B — Level 3 Reading
Question Booklet
The Dwarf and the Tall Man
and Teamwork in Nature

FIRST NAME	

SCORE		LEVEL	

Practice questions

page 2

A.   What did the tall man do with the dwarf's drums?

....

....

B.   Who was very strong?

[ ] the tall man   [ ] the dwarf

[ ] the Queen   [ ] the guard

The Dwarf and the Tall Man

> These questions are about *The Dwarf and the Tall Man*.

1. Who did the Queen hear when she was walking through the city?

    ☐ The guards   ☐ A shopkeeper

    ☐ Some horses   ☐ The dwarf and the tall man

    1 mark

2. Why do you think the dwarf was angry?

    ....

    ....

    ....

    1 mark

3. What was special about the prison?

    ....

    ....

    1 mark

4.   Why did the dwarf and the tall man smile?

....

....

....

5.   **"Look," cried the dwarf, "It's right up there on the wall."**
Why do you think the writer used the word 'cried' instead of
using the word 'said'?

....

....

....

6.   Why do you think the tall man laughed when the dwarf slid down the wall?

....

....

Questions on page 6 of the story

7.   How did the tall man and the dwarf manage to get the key?

....

....

....

8. How do you think the tall man and the dwarf felt when they had got the key down from the wall?

....

....

....

1 mark

9. What did the Queen think the dwarf and the tall man were doing?

....

1 mark

10. Look at page 6.
Which sentences tell you that the dwarf and the tall man worked together?

....

....

....

1 mark

11 Why do you think the Queen chuckled as she rode away?

....

....

....

1 mark

12. Put these sentences in the right order by numbering them from 1 to 6.
The first one has been done for you.

.... The Queen saw the dwarf and the tall man having a party.

.... The dwarf couldn't climb the wall.

...1.... The dwarf and the tall man were arguing.

.... The dwarf and the tall man escaped.

.... The man and the dwarf managed to get the key together.

.... The Queen had the dwarf and the tall man arrested.

2 marks

13. How has the way the dwarf and the tall man felt about each other changed by the end of the story?

....

....

....

....

2 marks

14. What do you think is the main idea of the story?

☐ Sometimes it's best to work together.   ☐ All dwarves are very strong.

☐ You shouldn't put people in prison.   ☐ Parties are good.

1 mark

These questions are about *BEE FACTS*

15. How many different types of bee are there?

....

....

1 mark

16. Which bees build the nest that all the bees live in?

....

....

1 mark

17. What will happen if the Queen bee gets too hot or too cold?

....

....

1 mark

These questions are about *ANT FACTS*

18.   What is the name of the ants who defend the ant nest?

....

....

1 mark

19.   How do ants manage to carry very heavy pieces of food?

....

....

1 mark

20.   How do Army ants make nests at night?

☐ Out of sticks and leaves.   ☐ They dig holes in the ground.

☐ By clinging together.   ☐ They use nests left
                                        by other insects.

1 mark

These questions are about *Teamwork in Nature*

21. Which page tells you what the whole booklet is about?

....

....

1 mark

Set A — Level 3 Reading
Story Booklet
The Grateful Crane

The Grateful Crane

Once upon a time, a poor young man lived in a cottage in the countryside. It was winter and the snow fell on the land, covering it in a thick, white blanket.

One day, the man was hunting when he heard a strange, groaning sound coming from a field. He walked towards the noise and found a crane caught in a rabbit trap. The man took pity on the crane and carefully opened the trap, taking out the crane's leg. The crane stopped groaning and looked at the man for a while before lifting up into the air and spreading its wings. The man watched it fly away towards the sunset.

The man returned home to his cold, dark cottage. He was lonely and he had no money to buy candles or firewood. No one ever visited him. He went to bed, tired after his day hunting. He was just falling asleep when there was a knock at the door.

"Who could be calling at my door so late at night?" he wondered. He opened the door and found a beautiful young woman in his doorway. Her feet were bare and she wore a long white dress. The man was astonished.
"My name is Tsu," she said. "I'm lost – would you please let me shelter here for the night?"

Tsu stayed at the cottage that night. And the next night too.
And the night after that.

Soon, the young man asked Tsu to marry him and she agreed at once.
Although the couple were poor, they were very happy. Everyone in the village
was delighted they had found happiness. Yet still the snow continued to fall
and the winter grew colder.

One day, the man found he had no money left to buy food. He did not know
how he and his wife could go on living. Tsu saw how sad her husband was and
made up her mind to weave a piece of cloth.

"Prepare a room for me to work in," she told him. "But you must not peep in."
The man promised that he would not and he set about preparing a loom for
her to work at.

Tsu shut herself in the room and began
to weave. For two days and nights, the
man waited. Finally, at the end of the
third day, his wife brought him the cloth.
She was thin and exhausted but the cloth
was the most wonderful and rare piece
the man had ever seen. His eyes grew
wide with amazement. The pattern was
the most beautiful the man had ever
seen and the colours shone more
brightly than the feathers of a peacock.
The man travelled from the village to the
nearest town and was able to sell the
precious cloth for a great sum of money.

The man and his wife lived happily for a while, using the money to buy food and firewood. But the long winter continued and slowly the money ran out. Tsu decided to weave another piece of cloth. She warned her husband again not to peep in as she closed the door to the weaving room. Three days and nights went by and the man started to grow worried. But, on the night of the fourth day, Tsu appeared. She was pale and more exhausted than before but the cloth she was holding was more magnificent than the first. The next morning, the man was able to sell the cloth for an amount of money greater than he could ever have dreamed of.

The man and his wife were very happy together. Thanks to Tsu's weaving, their life was more comfortable but soon the young man began to wish he had more and more money. Whenever the man went into the village, his neighbours questioned him over and over about his wife and her weaving.

"How strange it is," they said, "that she can weave a piece of cloth without ever buying a single thread!" The man too had been wondering about this but he had no answer for the villagers.

Soon, when his desire for more money became too great, he asked Tsu to make another piece of cloth. She did not see why they needed more money as they had plenty to last them for a long time. Reluctantly, Tsu agreed to weave just one more piece of cloth.

"You must not peep in," Tsu said, reminding the man of his promise. She closed the door behind her and set about her work.

Three days and nights passed. The young man grew impatient. He longed to know how his wife made the cloth. His curiosity finally overcame him and, forgetting the promise he had made, he crept quietly up to the door where his wife was at work. Gently and silently, he opened the door just wide enough to peep through.

The man covered his mouth as he let out a gasp, for he could not believe what he saw. Instead of his wife, there stood a crane, tearing out its feathers one by one and weaving them into a beautiful cloth.

The bird heard the man gasp and turned back into Tsu, his wife. She then told him her amazing story. She was the crane he had saved from death in the rabbit trap. She had returned as a young woman to repay the man for his kindness. Weaving the cloth had been painful and her body was bruised and thin. Now that her husband had broken his promise and knew the truth about her, she could no longer stay with him. The young man was truly sorry and he wished there was some way to change what he had done. Tsu changed back into an elegant white crane and flew away from the cottage, vanishing forever into the glowing orange sky.

The Grateful Crane   In Japan, this story is called *Tsuru No Onegaeshi*.

KS1/En/Levels 3/Set A — Reading: Story

EHP11

8

© *CGP 2002*

Set C

KEY STAGE 1
Levels 1–3

Spelling Test
Paper

Spelling

Dear Cinderella

Spelling Test Paper

Dear Cinderella

Instructions:

- find a quiet place where you can sit down with your child

- make sure you have all the necessary equipment to complete the test paper

- read the short piece of text on page 18 of the Instructions & Answers Booklet to your child twice in its entirety

- during the first reading, your child should not write anything in this booklet

- during the second reading, pause after each word to be tested (shown in bold type), to enable your child to write the word in the gap in this booklet

Time:

Take as long as necessary to complete the test paper.

Note to Parents:

See the Instructions and Answers Booklet for details on how to administer the test.

	Max.	**Number of words correct**
Score	20	....

See page 19 of the Answers Booklet for the spelling test mark conversion chart.

First name _____

Last name _____

_____ **Dear** _____ Ci

We are _____

_____ yo

We have to do all the

other day our wicked

Last week we had to

finished our work it b

dresses had _____

We are both hoping

prince having _____

the whole world.

It _____

lonely. We would lov

Maybe we _____

Love _____

The Ugly _____

xxx

erella, (practice question)

__ sorry for being horrible to you _____ you lived with us. We

 lot now that you _____ in the palace with the prince.

_aning, _____ and ironing now. It is _____ not fair! The

_pmother _____ made us mop the _____.

ng all the washing outside in the _____ and as soon as we had

_an to rain. We felt very _____, especially as our _____

_____ ruined!

 one _____ we will meet a prince just like you did. When is the

_____ ball? We will make sure we wear the most beautiful glass slippers in

_ice if you could come and visit us _____ sometimes we are

 hear all about your new life in the palace. Do you have servants and maids?

_____ come and _____ for you one day?

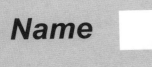

Name

Score

Level

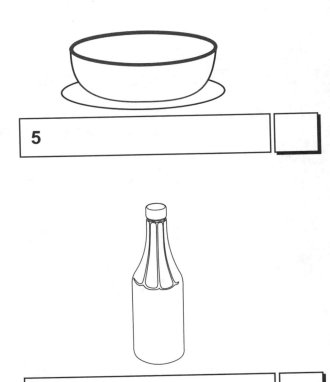

5

4

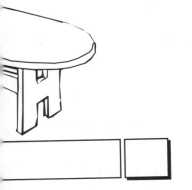

The Gingerbread Man

One day, an old woman made a gingerbread man with raisins

1 ☐ for .... and sweets for buttons.

1 ☐ When it was .... , the gingerbread man leapt

1 ☐ up off the .... and escaped through the door.

1 ☐ The old woman .... to catch him. She ran as

fast as she could, but the gingerbread man was too fast.

1 ☐ The gingerbread man kept .... He ran past a

1 ☐ group of farmers. "Stop, stop. We'll .... you

all up!" they shouted. The gingerbread man laughed as he

dodged under their legs. The gingerbread man thought he

1 ☐ was a really .... biscuit.

A fox came dashing by.

1 ☐ "I won't hurt you!" he said, "I'm .... chased by

a hunter. Let's get across the river and we'll both be safe."

Part 2

The gingerbread man jumped onto the fox's ....

as the fox leapt into the river.

"I'm sinking!" cried the fox. "Quick, ... biscuit,

jump onto my nose!" The gingerbread man jumped onto the

fox's nose and they reached the other side safely.

.... , the fox tossed up his head.

SNAP! went the .... of the fox.

SLURP! went his big, wet tongue.

"Help, help!" said the gingerbread man, "I'm almost

.... !"

"Mmm, tasty," said the fox, with a .... on his face.

But the gingerbread man said .... at all.

Spelling Mark	
out of 20 for parts 1 and 2	

Set A — Spelling
The Gingerbread Man

**Practice
question**

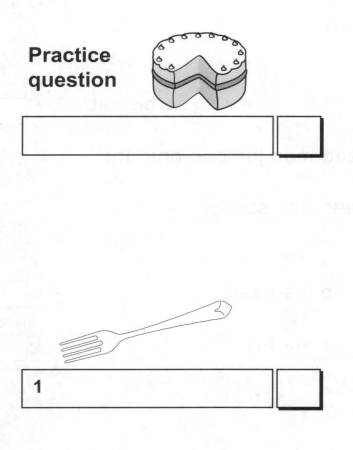

1

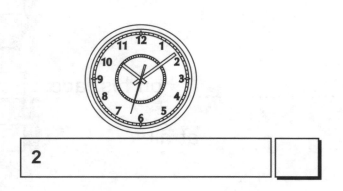

2

3

Fingerprints

If you dip your finger in ink, and press it onto a piece of paper, it will leave a fingerprint.

Everybody's fingers have a pattern of tiny marks on them, so small you can hardly see them.   Each person has their own different pattern, called a fingerprint.

A fingerprint shows the pattern of marks. When detectives find a fingerprint, the first thing they do is make a copy.

Then they try to match it to their records, to see who it belongs to.

If they find a fingerprint, then they can usually work out who was at the scene of the crime.

19 What do everybody's fingers have on them?

[ ] ink

[ ] a pattern of their family

[✓] a pattern of tiny marks

[ ] different people

[ ]

20 What do detectives do **first** when they find a fingerprint?

do a copy

[ ]

Taking a Fingerprint

Fingerprints

You will need   1 ink pad
1 box of tissues
sheets of paper

1)   Find a person whose fingerprint you want to take.

2)   Make sure the finger you are going to print is clean and dry.

3)   Open the ink pad and press the finger down onto it.
Make sure the whole of the top bit touches the ink.

4)   Lift the finger off carefully. Don't rush it. Close the ink pad.

5)   Press the finger down on a sheet of paper.
Try not to move it around or you will smudge the fingerprint.

6)   Count to ten then lift the finger off carefully.
Write the name of the person next to their fingerprint.

Use the tissue to clean the finger afterwards.

21 Why do you think the finger needs to be clean and dry?

.... ☐

22 Which part of the finger needs to touch the ink?

☐   the whole of the top bit   ☐   the left side

☐   the whole finger   ☐   the front of the finger   ☐

23 How do you know when to lift the finger off the paper?

.... ☐

24 What does it say you should do **after** you lift the finger off?

☐   arrest the person   ☐   smudge the fingerprint

☐   write the name of the person   ☐   press the finger down   ☐

25 Why do detectives take fingerprints?

☐ because they like them   ☐ to put in a book

☐ to find footprints   ☐ to try to find out who was
                                       at the crime scene   ☐

26 Thinking of what you have read in this booklet, do you think that Sarah
and Pete from the story "Footprints in the Garden" are good detectives?

☐ Yes   ☐ No

Why? (Give 2 reasons) ....

.... ☐

....

.... ☐

Set A — Level 2 Reading
Detectives

Name	
Score	Level and grade

Footprints in the Garden

It was the first clear day for ages.

Pete was playing in the garden with his sister, Sarah. Before today, it had been raining for three whole days, and the ground was muddy and wet. Pete didn't mind the mud. In fact, he quite liked it.

Then he saw the strange footprints.

Practice questions

A   What was Pete doing in the garden?

☐ He was hiding from his sister.　　☑ He was playing with his sister.

☐ He was eating worms.　　☐ He was in the shed.

B   How did Peter feel about the mud?

Not Bad

Just behind the garden shed, Pete could see a trail of footprints in the mud. He called out to Sarah.

"Look at these footprints," he yelled. Sarah came running over.

1 What did Pete find behind the garden shed?

☐ his sister   ☐ a football

☑ footprints   ☐ a cat

2 Who did Pete call out to?

........~~toyeld~~ sera...

Sarah looked at the first mark. It was shaped like a large foot.
She put her foot next to it. Alongside the print, her foot seemed very
small.

"These footprints are really big," said Pete. "They weren't made by us."

"Perhaps it was a burglar," suggested Sarah.

Pete thought for a moment. "We'd better look for some more clues,"
he said. "Let's follow the trail, and see where the footprints lead."

---

3   What did Sarah do to test the size of the footprint?

☐   She took off her shoe.   ☐   She used a tape measure.

☑   She put her foot next to it.   ☐   She put her hand in it.   ☐

4   Why did Pete want to follow the trail of footprints?

....   ☐

They started to follow the trail of footprints.

First they went through the vegetable patch.

"Don't stand on the vegetables," whispered Sarah. Carefully, Pete and Sarah tried to tiptoe over the soil, but it was thick and muddy.

Then the footprints went on through the flower beds.

"Don't walk on the flowers," warned Sarah. "Mum told us not to."

"But we've got to follow the footprints," said Pete.

5   Write down **two places** where Pete and Sarah followed the footprints.

    veg Pach and flower-
    beds

6   Why did Sarah say, "Don't walk on the flowers?"

☐ because she was scared   ☐ because she liked the flowers

☐ because she didn't like Pete   ☑ because Mum told them not to

Carefully, they walked through the flower bed, trying not to step on the flowers.

Soon they reached the top of the garden, where the big hedge grew. The footprints carried on up to the compost heap. Then they turned around and went back towards the house.

"Quick!" said Pete. "The burglar must be in the house."

Sarah and Pete ran back down the garden, through the compost heap, over the flower beds, through the vegetable patch and back over the lawn.

The big, muddy footprints led right up the path to the kitchen door.

Sarah and Pete hurried to the kitchen and rushed inside.

"MUM!" they both yelled. "There's a burglar in the house. We followed his footprints and they led us back here."

7   What was growing at the top of the garden?

.... P o o .... ☐

8   Where did the footprints go after they had turned around?

☑ back towards the house   ☐ to the compost heap

☐ to the big hedge   ☐ to the shed   ☐

9   Why do you think Sarah and Pete ran back down the garden?

.... they thought .... ☐

10   Why do you think MUM is written in capital letters?

☐ to show it is a new word   ☐ because it is the first
                                      word

☑ to show that Sarah and   ☐ so the burglar can hear   ☐
   Pete are yelling

Mum looked at them both, surprised. Then she pointed to a large pair of wellington boots, standing by the door on a piece of newspaper.

"Then here's the final clue," she said. "Did the footprints come from those boots?" Sarah and Pete looked at the boots. They were very big, and at the bottom they were covered in mud.

"I think so," said Pete, quietly.

"In that case, the footprints belong to your Dad, not to a burglar," laughed Mum. She looked at Pete and Sarah's muddy wellies. "You'd better take your boots off, and get cleaned up."

Pete and Sarah looked sad. They took off their wellies and coats.

"Can you solve another mystery?" asked Mum. Sarah and Pete looked up eagerly.   "Let's see if you can work out what's for tea."

Pete looked around the kitchen. "I can see a mixing bowl," he said.

"That's one clue," said Mum. Sarah sniffed the air.

"I can smell chocolate, " she said.

"That's two clues," said Mum.

"Chocolate cake!" shouted Sarah and Pete together. And they were right. Mum brought the cake out of the oven and put it on the table. And they all sat down for tea.

11 What did Mum point to?

☐ a large pair of gloves ☑ a large pair of wellington boots

☐ a newspaper ☐ the back door ☐

12 Who did the footprints in the garden belong to?

☑ Dad ☐ Sarah

☐ Mum ☐ the burglar ☐

13 Why do you think Pete and Sarah looked sad?

.... they thort it was an ....
.... oval Mum .... ☐ ☐

14 How do you think Sarah and Pete felt **at the end of the story**?

☐ cold ☑ happy

☐ dirty ☐ sad ☐

All About Detectives

In the first part of the booklet, you read a story called *Footprints in the Garden*, about two children looking for clues. In the next part of the booklet, you are going to read about detectives. There is some information about detectives and a list of instructions for how to take fingerprints.

Practice questions

A   What will the next part of the booklet tell you about?

☑ detectives   ☐ cats

☐ burglars   ☐ Pete and Sarah

B   What are you going to read in the next part of the booklet?

Tick **2** things.

a story   ....

information   ✓...............

a poem   ....

a letter   ....

instructions   ...✓...........

jokes   ....

Introduction

Detectives are people who investigate crimes. It is their job to find out what happened, and who was involved.

Some detectives work for the police. They don't wear uniforms.

Other detectives work for themselves.
People pay them to find out information —
like where a lost pet has gone.

15 What are detectives?

.......ınVestıgaters.. ☐

16 Who do some detectives work for?

☑ the police   ☐ the school

☐ the fire-brigade   ☐ the army   ☐

Looking for clues

The secret of being a good detective is looking for clues. They can be things like footprints or fingerprints left at the scene of a crime.

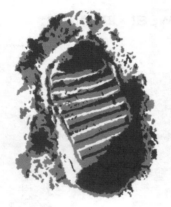

Footprints

If detectives find a footprint, they can work out what kind of person was at the scene. They can see whether the person had big or small feet, and sometimes even the make of the shoe.

An even better type of clue is a fingerprint.

---

17   What is the secret of being a good detective?

☐ using a magnifying glass   ☐ looking for people

☐ looking for shoes   ☑ looking for clues

18   What kind of clues might a detective look for?

Tick **2** things:

shoes   ....

footprints   ...✓...........

paintings   ....

fingerprints   ......✓........

Set B — Level 3 Reading
Story Booklet
The Dwarf and the Tall Man

The Dwarf and the Tall Man

by Isabell Lincoln

"And don't go making a noise this early in the morning ever again," shouted the tall man, as he threw the dwarf's drums into the river.

The tall man and the dwarf lived next door to each other, but they were always arguing.

The tall man complained that the dwarf was always playing his drums and noisily lifting weights. The dwarf did a lot of weightlifting. He was very strong, but very short.

The dwarf moaned that the tall man was always having noisy parties late at night.

"They're at it again!" thought their neighbours, who were getting fed up with all the arguments.

One day the Queen was riding through the city. As she rode down the street she heard the dwarf and the tall man arguing. She rode over to see what was happening.

"I'm sick of your late night parties," howled the dwarf. "They keep me awake." And, with that, he picked up a beer mug and bashed the tall man on the knee with it.

"This won't do at all," thought the Queen. "Not at all."

"Arrest them and take them to the prison!" she ordered her guards.

The dwarf and the tall man grumbled all the way to the prison. When they got there, the prison guard locked them up.

"This is a special prison," he said. "Inside it there is a key to the door. If you can find the key, you'll be able to use it to escape."

The tall man and the dwarf smiled. They thought they'd be able to get the key and escape.

As soon as the guard had locked the dwarf and the tall man into the prison, they started looking for the key.

It didn't take them long to find it.

"Look!" cried the dwarf. "It's up there, on the wall."

He started trying to climb up, but he slid right back down again.

"The wall's greased." the tall man laughed. "You'll never be able to climb up there."

The dwarf was disappointed and sulked in the corner.

The tall man jumped up, and after a couple of tries, he managed to reach the key.

"Would you believe it?" the tall man grumbled. "The key's stuck on so hard that I can't pull it off."

The tall man looked at the dwarf and his strong muscles.

"You could pull it off," said the tall man.

The dwarf looked at the tall man and his long arms.

"And you could lift me up there," said the dwarf.

"All right," said the tall man. "I'll do it."

The tall man picked up the dwarf, and held him so he could reach the key. With a great tug, the dwarf pulled the key off the wall.

The tall man put the dwarf on the ground. The tall man unlocked the door, and then the pair burst out of the prison, and ran home free.

The next evening, the tall man and the dwarf were making a lot of noise. "They're at it again," thought their neighbours.

Then the Queen rode past. She stopped to find out what all the noise was about.

"I thought you two were in prison," she said. "Why are you arguing again?"

"We're not arguing," said the dwarf.

"We're having a party," said the tall man.

"But how did you escape?" asked the Queen.

"I couldn't have done it without him." said the dwarf.

"And I couldn't have done it without him." said the tall man.

And the Queen rode away, chuckling to herself.

With thanks to Isabell Lincoln for permission to
reproduce *The Dwarf and the Tall Man*

Key Stage 1
English

Answer and Instruction Book

SATS Practice Papers
Levels 1-3

Contents
Using the Practice Papers P2-3
Levels P4-5
Answers Set A P6
Answers Set B P10

These practice papers won't make you better at English

... but they will show you what you **can** do, and what you **can't** do.

The papers are just like the ones you'll get on the day of the test — so they'll tell you what you need to **work at** if you want to do **better**.

Do a test, **get it marked** and look at what you **got wrong**.
That's the stuff you need to learn.

Go away, **practise** those tricky bits, then **do the <u>same</u> test again**.
If you're **still** doing badly on any bits, you'll have to do even **more practice** and test yourself **again**.

It doesn't sound like a lot of **fun**, but it **really will help**.

There are two big ways to improve your score

1) **Keep practising the things you get wrong**
   If you keep doing badly on the **information** questions, practise doing information questions. If you keep making a hash of the **spelling** questions, practise **spelling**. And so on...

2) **Don't throw away easy marks**
   Even if a question looks dead simple you still have to check your answer and make sure it's sensible.

Doing the Tests

There are **two sets** of practice papers in this pack.
Each set has:

Reading Test — level 2

      (one booklet with a story,   30 marks
      information and questions)

Reading Test — level 3

      (one information booklet, one story   25 marks
      booklet and one question booklet)

Spelling Test

      (one booklet to write answers in)   7 marks

*Get someone to read out the spelling
test for you (on pages 6-7 and 10-11
of this book). You have to fill in the
missing words on your answer sheet.*

1)   It's a good idea to do the tests more than once, and see if you can improve your mark. Write your answers on some separate paper if you do this.

2)   There are no **time limits**. The reading papers normally take no more than 45 minutes for each level, and the spelling test normally takes about 30 minutes. **But** it's fine to spend more or less time on them.

Follow all the instructions

1) The most important thing is to **understand** the questions.
     Read everything really **carefully** to be sure you're doing what they want.

2) **Write neatly**. You want the person who marks your work to be able to read it.

How to Mark Your Paper

It's **easy**. Use the answers in this booklet to mark the answers for each test.

When you've done a **complete** practice paper, you can use the tables below to look up your levels in reading and spelling.

Spelling Level

Just look up the number of marks you got in this table.

Number of Marks	Score	Spelling Level
0 → 2	1	Level 1 not achieved
3 → 5	2	1
6 → 8	3	
9 → 11	4	2
12 → 14	5	
15 → 17	6	
18 → 20	7	3

Reading Level

First of all, mark your level 2 paper.
Then you can look up how you've done in this table.

Number of Marks	Reading Level
0 ➔ 7	Level 2 not achieved
8 ➔ 18	2C
19 ➔ 24	2B
25 ➔ 30	2A

If you got a level 2, you also need to do the **level 3 paper**. If you get 15 marks or more in that, then you've got level 3. If you got less than 15 marks, then you've got whatever you got in the level 2 test.

Important!

Getting a particular level on one of these practice papers is **no guarantee** of getting it in the real SAT — **but** it's a pretty good guide.

Set A — Spelling Test Instructions and Answers

The Gingerbread Man

Part 1

Make sure the child has the spelling booklet. For the first part, go through the pictures one by one with them, and check they know what each one is supposed to be (the words are below). Then they have to write the object names in the boxes. As they do the test, check they still remember what each object is — you can tell them as many times as they need.

Answers:

Practice word	cake	3	table
1	fork	4	bottle
2	clock	5	bowl

Give **1 mark** for each word spelt correctly.

Part 2

For the second part of the test, you have to read out the whole passage. Read it out all the way through once, then tell the child that they have to fill in the blanks in their copy. Read it out again, pausing after each word in bold. You can repeat the words in bold as many times as is needed.

When you mark the test, give **1 mark** for each word spelt correctly.

One day, an old woman made a gingerbread man with raisins for .... **eyes** .... and sweets for buttons.

When it was .... **cooked** ...., the gingerbread man leapt up off the .... **tray** .... and escaped through the door. The old woman .... **tried** .... to catch him. She ran as fast as she could, but the gingerbread man was too fast.

The gingerbread man kept .... **running** .... He ran past a group of farmers. "Stop, stop. We'll .... **eat** .... you all up!" they shouted. The gingerbread man laughed as he dodged under their legs. The gingerbread man thought he was a really ....**clever**........ biscuit.

A fox came dashing by.

"I won't hurt you!" he said, " I'm ....**being**........ chased by a hunter. Let's get across the river and we'll both be safe."

The gingerbread man jumped onto the fox's ....**back**........ as the fox leapt into the river.

"I'm sinking!" cried the fox. "Quick, ...**little**........ biscuit, jump onto my nose!" The gingerbread man jumped onto the fox's nose and they reached the other side safely.

........**Suddenly**........ , the fox tossed up his head.

SNAP! went the ....**jaws**........ of the fox.

SLURP! went his big, wet tongue.

"Help, help!" said the gingerbread man, "I'm almost ....**gone**........ !"

"Mmm, tasty," said the fox, with a ....**smile**........ on his face.

But the gingerbread man said ....**nothing**........ at all.

Detectives

A	—	He was playing with his sister.	**Practice Questions**
B	—	He liked it.	
1	*1 mark*	Footprints.	
2	*1 mark*	Sarah / his sister.	
3	*1 mark*	She put her foot next to it.	
4	*1 mark*	To look for more clues / To see where the footprints led.	
5	*2 marks*	Vegetable patch Flower beds	
6	*1 mark*	Because Mum told them not to.	
7	*1 mark*	Big hedge.	
8	*1 mark*	Back towards the house.	
9	*1 mark*	Answers should refer to something sensible: eg They thought the burglar was in the house / They were worried about mum — answers solely about feelings are not acceptable (eg They were scared) unless a reason is given for why they were scared / worried.	
10	*1 mark*	To show that Sarah and Pete are yelling.	
11	*1 mark*	A large pair of wellington boots.	
12	*1 mark*	Dad.	
13	*2 marks*	Answers should refer to their disappointment at the end of the mystery and a sensible reason eg Because there wasn't a burglar / they were wrong about the burglar / they were sad the mystery was solved / they didn't want to stop playing / they didn't want to clean up.	
14	*1 mark*	Happy.	

A	—	Detectives.	**Practice Questions**
B	—	Information Instructions	
15	*1 mark*	People who investigate crimes — comments that don't come from the text are not acceptable.	
16	*1 mark*	The police.	
17	*1 mark*	Looking for clues.	
18	*2 marks*	Footprints Fingerprints	
19	*1 mark*	A pattern of tiny marks.	
20	*1 mark*	Make a copy — not "match it to records". "Make a copy and match it to records" is not acceptable.	
21	*1 mark*	Answers along the lines of: It could smudge/You wouldn't get a clear print/The ink would run. "It wouldn't work" is not acceptable — a specific reason should be given.	
22	*1 mark*	The whole of the top bit.	
23	*1 mark*	Count to ten.	
24	*1 mark*	Write the name of the person.	
25	*1 mark*	To try to find out who was at the crime scene.	
26	*2 marks*	Answer can be Yes OR No — 1 mark for each reason. No = Because they didn't realise it was their Dad / They didn't solve the mystery / They missed lots of clues Yes = They found the footprints / They followed the footprints / They worked out there was a chocolate cake.	

Set A — Level 3 Reading Answers

Japan & The Grateful Crane

1	1 mark	He opened the trap. OR He took the crane's leg out of the trap.
2	1 mark	Watched it fly away.
3	1 mark	Because no one ever visited him. OR Because it was so late.
4	1 mark	Because the young man and Tsu had found happiness.
5	1 mark	Because it was precious / rare / very beautiful / wonderful.
6	1 mark	Because it is more interesting OR Because it shows how beautiful the cloth was.
7	1 mark	Tsu could weave a piece of cloth without ever buying a piece of thread.
8	2 marks	Give two marks for answer with good reason, for example: yes He has broken his promise. / no He thought he'd just see his wife in the room yes He should have trusted Tsu. / no He really wanted to see Tsu weaving OR either or no box ticked He didn't think he was, but he was breaking a promise. Give one mark for answer restating question, for example: yes He was wrong to look. / no He was not wrong to look.
9	1 mark	He becomes happier / He lives more comfortably / He has more money / He has a wife.
10	1 mark	To repay the man's kindness. OR To thank the man for freeing her from the trap OR To say thank you for saving her life.
11	1 mark	(a) He would feel sad / sorry for what he had done / lonely.
	1 mark	(b) Any good and appropriate answer, such as: He has lost his wife OR He knows he'll never see her again. OR She'll never come back. OR This time, the crane is his wife not a bird. OR He was sorry for what he had done.

12	1 mark	The Sun.
13	1 mark	The Land of the Rising Sun.
14	1 mark	It is shorter. OR It is less colourful. OR You wear it over trousers. OR The man ties the knot at the side.
15	1 mark	A long belt.
16	1 mark	Because Japanese people are very polite.
17	1 mark	Eating Smarties.
18	2 marks	Slurp OR Make slurping noises. [1 mark] Because Japanese people would think it strange if you were quiet. [1 mark]
19	1 mark	Salmon or tuna.
20	1 mark	A tea towel.
21	1 mark	Obi and Geta.
22	1 mark	6

Set B — Spelling Test Instructions and Answers

> ## Candyfloss

Part 1

Make sure the child has the spelling booklet. For the first part, go through the pictures one by one with them, and check they know what each one is supposed to be (the words are below). Then they have to write the object names in the boxes. As they do the test, check they still remember what each object is — you can tell them as many times as they need.

Answers:

Practice word	cat	**3**	moon
1	cow	**4**	slide
2	bird	**5**	boat

Give **1 mark** for each word spelt correctly.

Part 2

For the second part of the test, you have to read out the whole passage. Read it out all the way through once, then tell the child that they have to fill in the blanks in their copy. Read it out again, pausing after each word in bold. You can repeat the words in bold as many times as is needed.

Give **1 mark** for each word spelt correctly.

Every year, thousands of people visit Blackpool.

Blackpool has a massive tower that looks out over the ....**sea**............ . The tower has been there for over a hundred years. The rest of the ....**town**............ has changed a lot since then.

Nowadays ....**there**............ are so many things to do in Blackpool, it would take ....**weeks**............ to see everything.

You can go on the biggest roller **coaster** in the country. You can **race** around a track in a go-kart, or go right up to the top of Blackpool Tower itself.

If it is **raining** or cold, you can go **ice** - skating. You can also go rock-climbing and trampolining **indoors** .

Most of the outdoor **rides** are closed in **winter** , but you can pretend that it is still summer at Sandcastle Water World. There are deep blue **pools** , waterfalls and huge **waves** .

At Blackpool, you can **buy** candyfloss even in the middle of winter. Just make **sure** you keep it out of the rain.

Set B — Level 2 Reading Answers

The Sea

A	—	Her pirate hat and eye-patch
B	—	Going exploring with the dog.

Practice Questions

1	*1 mark*	Glass **OR** Coloured glass **OR** Pretty pieces of coloured glass
2	*1 mark*	A bottle **OR** A sandy little bottle
3	*1 mark*	A sheet of paper **OR** A map
4	*1 mark*	She thought she had found a treasure map.
5	*1 mark*	Excited
6a	*1 mark*	A spade
6b	*1 mark*	Paws / his paws
7	*1 mark*	For tea **OR** It was time for dinner **OR** similar answer.
8	*1 mark*	She hadn't found any treasure.
9	*1 mark*	I'm sure you'll find some treasure. **OR** Have another look first thing tomorrow morning.
10	*1 mark*	She was too excited about finding treasure.
11	*1 mark*	Because she had found treasure. **OR** She'd found a package. **OR** To be heard.
12	*1 mark*	To show that Marla-May was very nervous and excited.
13	*2 marks*	**For 2 marks:** It was where the treasure map said it would be, and Marla-May thought the map was drawn by pirates. **OR** It had a parrot in, and pirates have parrots. **For 1 mark:** It was where the map said it would be. **OR** It had a parrot in.
14	*1 mark*	She hid the treasure there for Marla-May overnight.

     12

The Sea

A	—	Oceans.	**Practice Questions**
B	—	Sea Monsters.	
15	*1 mark*	Nearly three quarters.	
16	*1 mark*	Salt water.	
17	*2 marks*	Atlantic and Indian oceans (1 mark for each)	
18	*1 mark*	The Mariana Trench.	
19	*1 mark*	11 034 metres **OR** 11, 034 metres **OR** About eleven thousand metres.	
20	*1 mark*	In the ocean.	
21	*1 mark*	Because they were afraid of sea monsters / Kraken.	
22	*2 marks*	For one mark: an octopus For two marks: any additional information about the Kraken.	
23	*1 mark*	To catch the wind.	
24	*1 mark*	The ship will go faster.	
25	*1 mark*	Steers the ship.	
26	*1 mark*	The mast.	

Set B — Level 3 Reading Answers

Working Together

1	*1 mark*	The dwarf and the tall man.
2	*1 mark*	He'd been kept awake by the tall man's parties. **OR** The tall man had kept him awake. **OR** He hadn't got enough sleep. **OR** He was tired. **OR** The tall man's parties were very noisy.
3	*1 mark*	It had a key in it that opened the door. **OR** People were allowed to let themselves out if they could find the key.
4	*1 mark*	Because they thought they'd be able to get the key and escape. **OR** Because there was a key that would let them get out. **DON'T accept** because there was a key — answer must make some reference to it letting them escape/get out.
5	*1 mark*	Accept either: Because it's more interesting. **OR** To show that the dwarf said it loudly/excitedly **OR** To show that the dwarf was unhappy/disappointed.
6	*1 mark*	Because the dwarf couldn't get the key. **OR** Because the wall was greased/slippery.
7	*2 marks*	The tall man lifted the dwarf up [1 mark], and the dwarf pulled the key off the wall [1 mark].
8	*1 mark*	The dwarf and the tall man felt happy.
9	*1 mark*	arguing **OR** having an argument **OR** fighting
10	*1 mark*	When they both say "I couldn't have done it without him". **OR** any other clear reference to these sentences.
11	*1 mark*	Accept any from: She is happy that the dwarf and the tall man aren't fighting any more. She thinks it is funny that the dwarf and the tall man used to argue but now they're friendly. She is pleased that her plan (to make the dwarf and the tall man friends) worked. **OR** anything similar. Don't accept: She is happy **OR** She thinks it's funny (without any reference to why)
12	*2 marks*	6, 3, 1, 5, 4, 2 *[2 marks for all right, 1 mark for all but two right]*
13	*2 marks*	1 mark for saying that early in the story they didn't get on, 1 mark for saying that by the end they were friends.
14	*1 mark*	Sometimes it's best to work together.

Working Together

15	*1 mark*	Over 20 000 **OR** Over twenty thousand.
16	*1 mark*	The worker bees. Accept worker.
17	*2 marks*	She lays fewer eggs [1 mark] and the worker bees will move further away from or closer to her [1 mark]
18	*1 mark*	Soldier ants.
19	*1 mark*	They work as a team. **OR** They work together. **OR** Several ants lift it at once.
20	*1 mark*	By clinging together.
21	*1 mark*	Page 3 / The introduction.